Aural Time!

Practice Tests for the New Revised ABRSM Syllabus

Grade 3

DAVID TURNBULL

CONTENTS

Published by
Bosworth & Co. Limited
14-15 Berners Street,
London W1T 3LJ, UK.

Exclusive Distributors:
Music Sales Limited
Distribution Centre, Newmarket Road,
Bury St Edmunds, Suffolk IP33 3YB, UK.
Music Sales Pty Limited
20 Resolution Drive, Caringbah,
NSW 2229, Australia.

Order No. BOE100078
ISBN 978-1-84938-759-0

This book © Copyright 2010 Bosworth.
International Copyright Secured.

Printed in the EU.

Your Guarantee of Quality
As publishers, we strive to produce every book to the highest commercial standards.
This book has been carefully designed to minimise awkward page turns and to make playing from it a real pleasure.
Particular care has been given to specifying acid-free, neutral-sized paper made from pulps which have not been elemental chlorine bleached.
This pulp is from farmed sustainable forests and was produced with special regard for the environment.
Throughout, the printing and binding have been planned to ensure a sturdy, attractive publication which should give years of enjoyment.
If your copy fails to meet our high standards, please inform us and we will gladly replace it.

www.musicsales.com

BOSWORTH
part of The Music Sales Group

INTRODUCTION

Although aural skills are a discrete part of graded music examinations, it is important to encourage pupils to realise that well-focused listening lies at the heart of all music-making. Understanding the difference in sound between major and minor scales by accurately singing them will help pupils discover for themselves the notes needed to play the increasing repertoire of scales needed for Grade 3, as well as preparing them for minor-key examples in aural tests B and D at this grade.

Reluctant singers will gain in confidence if presented with a series of carefully graduated steps that they can take in their stride. For example, accurately singing up and down the first three degrees of major and minor scales, concentrating on the difference between the major 3rd and minor 3rd, offers excellent preparation for Test B. It is something that pupils can practise on their own at any convenient time and, once confident, the exercise can be extended to five notes and then the complete scale, before trying to echo the melodic phrases in Section B of this book.

In Test D, tonality is the additional feature that candidates might be asked to identify at Grade 3. Although examiners are likely to use simple language (such as "Is this piece in a major or minor key?") it is important to check that pupils understand that tonality refers to the key(s) of a passage of music. The term is likely to be used in later grades, and it is one that many students easily confuse with tone. Similarly, it is wise to ensure that pupils are totally clear about the meaning of terms encountered in earlier grades (dynamics, tempo and articulation), as these are easily muddled in the tension of an exam situation.

Formal practice of the set of all four tests should begin well before the date of the examination. In the early stages pupils should be encouraged to have a second attempt at any tests they find difficult, and teachers should use this as a diagnostic opportunity to spot where additional work may be needed. However, ultimately a good mark for aural will depend on a prompt, as well as accurate, response in all of the tests.

As not all good instrumental teachers are fluent pianists, most of the tests in this volume have simple piano accompaniments – if necessary, the left hand could be omitted and the examples played as melodic lines only. Teachers may like to use some of the tests in Section A as additional material for Section D by using varied dynamics and articulation, and by introducing variations in the tempo.

Paul Terry
London, 2010

Test A. Tapping Test.

GRADE 3

Clap the pulse of the piece of music, which will be in 2 (including 6/8), or 3 time (including 9/8), or 4 time. Join in with your clapping as soon as you can, stressing where the strong beats fall. You will be asked whether the music is in 2, 3 or 4 time, but not required to state the time signature.

2

Andante

Scottish trad.: *Will Ye No Come Back Again?*

Moderato

Breton trad.: *Pieds en l'air*

Allegro non troppo

French trad.: *La Mère Michel*

Moderato

Stephen Foster: *Massa's in de Cold, Cold Ground*

4

Maestoso

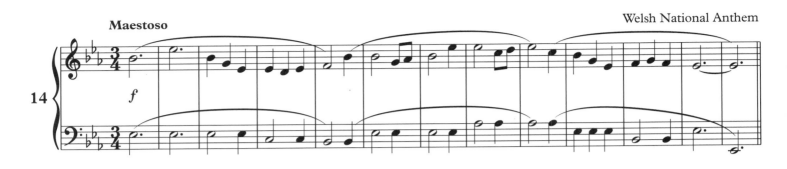

14

Moderato

J.S. Bach: *Jesu, Joy*

15

Allegro

American trad.: *John Brown's Body*

16

Moderato

Scottish Air: *Caller Herrin'*

17 *mf*

Lento

Russian trad.: *Song of the Volga Boatmen*

18 *mf*

Allegro

Music Hall song: *Daisy*

19 *f*

Moderato

Müller

20 *mf*

Test B. Echoes.

Sing, as echoes, three short phrases played to you. The echoes should follow each played phrase in strict time, without an intervening pause. The key-chord and the tonic will first be sounded and the pulse indicated.

Test C. Recognising Changes.

Recognise and explain or sing/clap a rhythmic or melodic change to a four-bar phrase in a major or minor key played over twice. The key-chord and tonic will first be sounded. If necessary, the phrase may be played again (though this will affect the assessment).

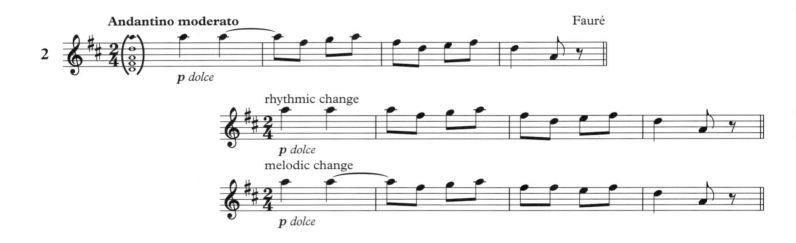

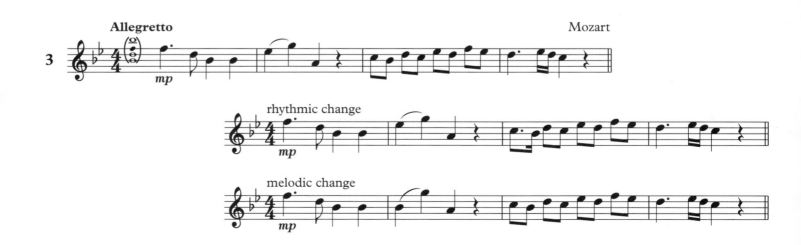

Test D. Recognising Features.

Identify certain features of a piece played over to you. The features will be confined to contrasted dynamics (*p/f*), gradation of tone (*crescendo/diminuendo*), articulation (*staccato/legato*) and recognition of tempo changes (*rallentando/accelerando* etc.) and recognition of major and minor modes. Use Italian terms in your answers where appropriate. The piece, or any section of it, can be repeated if neccessary.

Andante

Haydn: "*Surprise*" *Symphony*

Questions:
> a. Is the piece in a major or minor key?
> b. Is the music mostly *staccato* or *legato*?
> c. Which was the loudest part?
> d. Was it played at a steady tempo?

Lento

Schumann (adapted)

Questions:
> a. Is the piece in a major or minor key?
> b. Did the music get gradually louder or softer? If so, where?
> c. Was it mainly *legato*, *staccato*, or a mixture of both?
> d. Was it played at a steady tempo? If not, where did the tempo change?

B. & Co. Ltd., 22288

Allegro non troppo

Schumann (adapted)

Questions:

    a. Is the piece in a major or minor key?

    b. Did the music get gradually louder or softer? If so, where?

    c. Was it mainly *legato*, *staccato*, or a mixture of both?

    d. Was it played at a steady tempo? If not, where did the tempo change?

Allegretto

Purcell (adapted)

Questions:

    a. Describe the dynamics of the music.

    b. Does it begin *staccato* or *legato*?

    c. Does it end *staccato* or *legato*?

    d. Are there any alterations to tempo? If so where?

    e. Is it in a major or a minor key?

Moderato

Telemann (adapted)

Questions:
- a. Is the piece in a major or minor key?
- b. Describe the dynamics of the music.
- c. Was it mainly *legato,* or *staccato,* or a mixture of both?
- d. Was it played at a steady tempo? If not, where did the tempo change?

Moderato

Tchaikovsky (adapted)

Questions:
- a. Is the piece in a major or minor key?
- b. Describe the dynamics of the music.
- c. Was it mainly *legato,* or *staccato,* or a mixture of both?
- d. Was it played at a steady tempo? If not, where and how did the tempo change?

Czerny (adapted)

Questions:
  a. Is the piece in a major or minor key?
  b. Did the music get gradually louder or softer? If so, where?
  c. Was it mainly *legato*, *staccato*, or a mixture of both?
  d. Was it played at a steady tempo? If not, where did the tempo change?

Mendelssohn

Questions:
  a. Did the music start in a major or minor key?
  b. Did it end in a major or a minor key?
  c. Did the music become gradually louder or softer? If so, where?
  d. Was it played at a steady tempo? If not, where and how did the tempo change?

Questions:

    a. Did the tempo of the music alter? If so, how?

    b. Did the music begin *legato* or *staccato*?

    c. Was it in a major key or a minor key?

    d. Describe the dynamics.

(If playing the melodic line without accompaniment, play notes in brackets.)

Questions:

    a. Did the music start in a major key or a minor key?

    b. Did it end in a major key or a minor key?

    c. Was there any alteration in the tempo?

    d. Describe the dynamics of the music.

Other titles by David Turnbull...

Theory Time!	**Scale Time!**	**Singing Time!**
Grade 3	Grade 3	Grade 3
BOE004870	BOE004997	BOE005030

Available from

BOSWORTH
part of The Music Sales Group

Exclusive Distributors:
Music Sales Limited
Distribution Centre, Newmarket Road,
Bury St Edmunds, Suffolk IP33 3YB, UK.

www.musicsales.com